MY DAD
the Tuk Tuk Driver

BY LESLIE FALCONER • PHOTOGRAPHS BY KIRA MELISSE PHOTOGRAPHY

My dad
drives
a tuk tuk.

4

Many different families sit on his seat.

He takes care of others

like they
are his sisters
and brothers.

CAN YOU FIND my dad's tuk tuk?

My dad drives a tuk tuk.

Some families
are BIG.

Some families are small.

How many people are in
YOUR FAMILY?

My family is five in all.

My dad drives
a tuk tuk.

18

CAN YOU FIND
my dad's tuk tuk?

CAN YOU FIND my little sister?

20

Some families
are happy.
Some families
are sad.
My family
is excited
when we ride
with my dad.

Some families
go to the market.

Some families
go sightseeing.

My family goes to school.

I learn that whatever I do, just like my dad, I can take care of others too.

My dad drives
a tuk tuk.

Many different
families sit
on his seat.
He shows them
the way.
Maybe your
family can
ride with him
too someday.

more about CAMBODIA

CAMBODIA

PHNOM PENH

Tuk tuks are the most common form of urban transport in Cambodia. They get their name from the noise their engines make while idling.

Many tuk tuks are highly decorated, either painted or with hammered metal good luck charms.

Cambodians greet each other by pressing their palms together in front of their bodies and bowing. This is called a Sampeah.

The Cambodian flag is the only flag in the world that features a building.

The kouprey is a wild forest cow known for its long, curving horns. It is one of the rarest animals in the world and Cambodia's national animal.

Khmer, pronounced \ka-´mer\, is the official language of Cambodia. In addition to Khmer, French, Vietnamese, and English are also spoken.

Futbol (soccer) was introduced by the French, and is one of the most popular sports in Cambodia. Other sports, such as volleyball, field hockey, rugby, golf, and baseball, are also played here.

Cambodian children study math, history, geography, science, Khmer, English, French, art, music, and dance. Most students wear uniforms.

Cambodians eat rice at every meal. It's served fried, steamed, or in the form of noodles.

Pol Pot and the Khmer Rouge were some of the meanest people this world has ever known. Because of their actions, Cambodia still needs a lot of help to rebuild the educational system and family values.

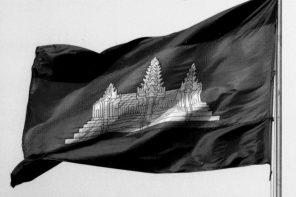